THE OFFICIAL
HULL CITY AFC
QUIZ BOOK

THE OFFICIAL HULL CITY AFC QUIZ BOOK

Compiled by Chris Cowlin
and Kevin Snelgrove

Foreword by Paul Duffen

APEX PUBLISHING LTD

Hardback first published in 2008 by

Apex Publishing Ltd
PO Box 7086, Clacton on Sea, Essex, CO15 5WN, England
www.apexpublishing.co.uk

British Library Cataloguing-in-Publication Data
A catalogue record for this book
is available from the British Library

ISBN HARDBACK: 1-906358-29-X   978-1-906358-29-7

Typeset in 10.5pt Chianti Bdlt Win95BT

Cover Design: Siobhan Smith

Printed and bound in Great Britain by
Biddles Ltd., King's Lynn, Norfolk

Author's Note:
Please can you contact me: ChrisCowlin@btconnect.com if you find any
mistakes/errors in this book as I would like to put them right on any
future reprints of this book. I would also like to hear from Hull City fans
who have enjoyed the test! For more information on me and my books
please look at: www.ChrisCowlin.com

This book is an official product of Hull City AFC

We would like to dedicate this book to:

The generations of Tigers fans that never got to see Hull City AFC play in the Premier League.

FOREWORD

I'm privileged to be asked to write the foreword for this book.

The history of Hull City is long and varied and I'm sure the questions included in this book will bring back plenty of memories.

Having been fortunate enough to see a preview of this book, I know that Hull City fans of all ages will be entertained for hours with questions about the Tigers past and present.

As we continue to write new chapters in the Club's history, it's always fitting to remember what went before.

I hope you all enjoy this wonderful quiz book as much as I did.

Best wishes
Paul Duffen
Chairman, Hull City AFC

INTRODUCTION

I would first of all like to thank Paul Duffen for writing the foreword to this book. I am very grateful for his help on this project.

I would also like to thank all the past legends of Hull City Football Club and many current employees of the club for their comments and reviews on this book (these can be found at the back of the book).

I would also like to thank Gill Wilkinson and Rob Smith for their help and advice during the books compilation.

I hope you enjoy this book. Hopefully it should bring back some wonderful memories!

It was great working with Kevin Snelgrove again, who is very well organised, between us I hope we have given you a selection of easy, medium and hard questions.

In closing, I would like to thank all my friends and family for encouraging me to complete this book.

Best wishes
Chris Cowlin

Visit Chris Cowlin's website:

www.ChrisCowlin.com

Visit Kevin Snelgrove's website:

www.KevinSnelgrove.co.uk

HISTORY OF THE CLUB

1.   In what year was the club formed?

2.   Can you name the stadium that Hull moved to in
        2002?

3.   At which ground did the club play between 1945 and
        2002?

4.   What is the club's nickname?

5.   In what year in their history did the club first play top-
        flight football?

6.   Following on from the previous question, which team
        did they beat 2-1 at home during their first ever top-
        flight League match?

7.   Which two colours do the club wear during their home
        matches?

8.   What is the name of the club's mascot?

9.   Which player holds the record for the most League
        appearances with 520?

10.   Against which team did Hull City play when they
        recorded their record home attendance of 55,019
        during February 1949?

NATIONALITIES – 1

Match up the Hull player with his nationality

11.	Boaz Myhill	English
12.	Geovanni Deiberson	Trinidad and Tobago
13.	Richard Garcia	Irish
14.	Nick Barmby	Dutch
15.	Caleb Folan	Welsh
16.	George Boateng	English
17.	Sam Ricketts	Australian
18.	Wayne Brown	Scottish
19.	Liam Cooper	Brazilian
20.	Tony Warner	Scottish

MANAGERS - 1

*Match the manager with the period he was
in charge at Hull City*

21.	Bob Brocklebank	1970-74
22.	Ambrose Langley	1991-97
23.	Terry Dolan	1916-21
24.	Ernest Blackburn	1923-31
25.	Terry Neill	2002-06
26.	Peter Taylor	1904-05
27.	Billy McCracken	1955-61
28.	Brian Horton	1936-46
29.	James Ramster	1984-88
30.	David Menzies	1905-13

SQUAD NUMBERS - 2008/2009 – 1

Match up the player with his squad number for the season

31.	Nathan Doyle	43
32.	Ryan France	5
33.	Will Atkinson	7
34.	Bryan Hughes	2
35.	Tom Woodhead	31
36.	Andy Dawson	11
37.	Craig Fagan	12
38.	Matt Duke	13
39.	John Welsh	3
40.	Wayne Brown	19

WHERE DID THEY COME FROM? – 1

Match up the player with the club from which he joined Hull City

41.	Richard Jobson	Blackpool
42.	Geovanni Deiberson	West Bromwich Albion
43.	Mick Hollifield	Dundee
44.	Syd Gerrie	Blackburn Rovers
45.	Derek Hood	Preston North End
46.	Bruce Bannister	Manchester City
47.	Kevin Gage	Wolves
48.	Mark Hateley	Watford
49.	Alex Dyer	Glasgow Rangers
50.	Bob Dewhurst	Plymouth Argyle

TOP TEN LEAGUE APPEARANCES

Match the player with the number of League appearances he made for Hull City

51.	Tommy Bleakley	365 (5)
52.	George Maddison	368
53.	Ken Wagstaff	430
54.	Garreth Roberts	372
55.	Billy Bly	520
56.	Matt Bell	368
57.	Andy Davidson	403
58.	Tony Norman	415
59.	Doug Clarke	374 (4)
60.	Chris Chilton	393

INTERNATIONAL CAPS

*Match the player with the number of caps
he earned for his country*

61.	Brian Marwood	4 caps for Holland
62.	Theodore Whitmore	25 caps for England
63.	Jay-Jay Okocha	54 caps for Scotland
64.	Tony Norman	105 caps for Jamaica
65.	Emlyn Hughes	3 caps for Northern Ireland
66.	Aidan Davidson	32 caps for England
67.	George Boateng	62 caps for England
68.	Billy Bremner	75 caps for Nigeria
69.	Mark Hateley	1 cap for England
70.	Stan Mortensen	5 caps for Wales

LEAGUE APPEARANCES – 1

Match up the player with the number of League appearances he made for the club

71.	Matt Bell	286 (2)
72.	Tony Brien	141
73.	Andy Flounders	135 (7)
74.	Dai Davies	393
75.	Stuart Croft	43 (4)
76.	Ken Houghton	55 (3)
77.	Gary Hobson	253 (11)
78.	Peter Skipper	126 (33)
79.	Ray Daniel	409 (5)
80.	Garreth Roberts	187 (3)

THE LEAGUE CUP

81. What was the aggregate score when Hull met Carlisle United in the 1st round during August 1995?

82. Who scored the only goal when Hull beat Grimsby Town 1-0 during the 1st round, 1st leg win during August 1989?

83. Which north London club knocked Hull out of the 2nd round, beating them 5-1 on aggregate during September and October 1988?

84. Which club did Hull beat 3-0 away in the 1st round during August 2007?

85. Following on from the previous question, can you name the three scorers?

86. Who scored a brace in the 3-0 home win in the 1st round, 2nd leg during September 1985 against Halifax Town?

87. Which team did Hull beat 1-0 away during August 2007 in the 2nd round, with Stuart Elliott scoring the only goal?

88. Who scored a brace in the 4-2 home win in the 2nd round during September 1975 against Preston North End?

89. Which club did Hull beat 4-1 at home during November 1973 in the 3rd round, with Phil Holme scoring twice?

90. Who scored the only goal in the 1-0 2nd round win against Fulham during September 1972?

GOALKEEPERS

Match the player with the period he spent at Hull City

91.	Billy Bly	1910-20
92.	George Maddison	2000-04
93.	Tony Norman	1924-38
94.	Martin Spendiff	1991-96
95.	Eddie Blackburn	1949-54
96.	Paul Musselwhite	1939-61
97.	Jeff Wealands	1905-08
98.	Nick Hendry	1974-80
99.	Tommy Forgan	1972-79
100.	Alan Fettis	1980-88

POSITIONS IN THE LEAGUE – 1

Match up the season with the position in which
Hull City finished in the League

101.	*2007/2008*	**24th in Division Two**
102.	*2005/2006*	**22nd in Division Three**
103.	*2003/2004*	**14th in Division Three**
104.	*2001/2002*	**9th in Division Two**
105.	*1999/2000*	**3rd in the Championship**
106.	*1997/1998*	**18th in the Championship**
107.	*1995/1996*	**2nd in League Two**
108.	*1993/1994*	**14th in Division Two**
109.	*1991/1992*	**14th in Division Two**
110.	*1989/1990*	**11th in Division Two**

THE CHAMPIONSHIP
PLAY-OFF FINAL – 2008

111. In what position in the League did Hull finish to compete in the play-offs?

112. Which team did City beat in the play-off semi-finals?

113. Following on from the previous question, Hull beat their opponents 2-0 away, but what was the score at home?

114. Following on from the previous question, can you name two of the goalscorers that scored for Hull City in the home match?

115. Which manager guided the club to this success?

116. Which team did City play in the final?

117. What was the score in the final?

118. Following on from the previous question, can you name the player who scored for Hull?

119. What was the attendance for the final at Wembley – 66,703, 76,703 or 86,703?

120. Can you name seven of Hull's starting eleven for the final match at Wembley?

BIG WINS – 1

Match up the fixture with Hull's high-scoring victory

121.	*v. Cardiff City, Home, League,* *February 1995*	*5-2*
122.	*v. Darlington, Home, League,* *October 1991*	*3-0*
123.	*v. Fulham, Home, League,* *November 1985*	*6-2*
124.	*v. Shrewsbury Town, Home, League,* *March 1986*	*5-0*
125.	*v. Rotherham United, Home, League,* *November 1993*	*4-3*
126.	*v. Leicester City, Home, League,* *November 1990*	*4-0*
127.	*v. Exeter City, Home, League,* *April 1994*	*4-1*
128.	*v. Leyton Orient, Away, League,* *November 1984*	*5-1*
129.	*v. Preston North End, Home, League,* *January 1973*	*5-2*
130.	*v. Swansea City, Home, League,* *May 1992*	*5-4*

WHO AM I?

131. I joined Hull from Ipswich Town in 2006 and made 35 League appearances, scoring 5 goals. I also made 4 appearances for England at Under-21 level.

132. I started my professional career at Blackpool in 1941, whom I went on to manage from 1967 to 1969. I played for Hull for 2 seasons from 1955 to 1957.

133. I was born in Derby in 1961. I played as centre forward and was the first non-Scottish player to win the Footballer of the Year in Scotland while playing for Rangers.

134. I made 587 League appearances for Leeds United before moving to Hull City in 1976. I captained Leeds and also my country Scotland.

135. For 5 consecutive seasons from 1966 to 1970 I was Hull's leading League goalscorer with a total of 103 League goals.

136. I was born in Jarrow in 1896. I started my career with the Tigers before moving to Chelsea in 1923.

137. I moved to newly promoted Hull in the summer of 2004 on a free transfer from Southend United. In 2006 I was transferred to Crystal Palace for £1.25 million.

138. I am a striker and started my professional career at Hull City in 1986 where I made 143 League appearances, scoring 55 League goals.

139. I was born in Romford, Essex, in 1973 and played for Arsenal and England. I moved to the Tigers in 2007.

140. I was born in Hull and scored the winning goal in the 2008 play-off final against Bristol City on 24 May at Wembley.

MANAGERS – 2

*Match the manager with the period he was
in charge at Hull City*

141.	John Kaye	1948-51
142.	Stan Ternent	1974-77
143.	Fred Stringer	1952-55
144.	Bob Jackson	1913-14
145.	Cliff Britton	1931-34
146.	Brian Little	1921-23
147.	Haydn Green	2000-02
148.	Harry Chapman	1989-91
149.	Raich Carter	1914-16
150.	Percy Lewis	1961-69

LEAGUE GOALSCORERS – 1

*Match up the player with the total number
of League goals scored for the club*

151.	Ray Henderson	193
152.	Linton Brown	1
153.	Alan Jarvis	3
154.	Keith Edwards	54
155.	Mark Hateley	9
156.	Lee Warren	173
157.	Chris Chilton	86
158.	Ken Wagstaff	18
159.	Gary Swann	24
160.	Andy Davidson	12

THE FA CUP

161. Who scored six goals against Whitby Town in the 1st round replay in November 1996?

162. Which two teams did Hull beat 1-0 in the 1st and 2nd rounds before losing to Chelsea in the 3rd round in January 1992?

163. Who scored both goals for the Tigers against Plymouth Argyle in the 3-2 defeat in the 3rd round during January 2008?

164. Which player scored in all three games during 1988/1989 in the 3rd, 4th and 5th rounds?

165. Who scored Hull's equaliser in the 1-1 home draw in the 3rd round during January 2007 against Middlesbrough?

166. Who scored a brace in the 2-2 home draw in the 3rd round in January 1986 against Plymouth Argyle?

167. Which London club did Hull beat 1-0 in the 4th round in February 1973, with Ken Houghton scoring?

168. Which Wales-based team did Hull beat 2-1 in the 3rd round during January 1989?

169. Which London team knocked City out of the FA Cup quarter-final after a replay during March 1966?

170. How many attempts did it take before Hull beat Darlington in the 2nd round during 1960/1961?

MATCH THE YEAR – 1

Match up the event with the correct year

171.	The club was formed	1997
172.	Stan Ternent was born	1966
173.	Phil Brown took over as the Tigers' manager	1984
174.	Hull were champions of Division Three	1946
175.	Brian Horton took over as Hull manager	2004
176.	Terry Neill was born	1961
177.	Nick Barmby joined the Tigers	1987
178.	Mark Hateley took over as Hull manager	2006
179.	Bob Brocklebank left as Hull manager	1942
180.	Wayne Jacobs signed for Hull City from Sheffield Wednesday	1904

1990s

181. Which manager left Hull City in November 1998?

182. In 1997 which former tennis player purchased Hull City?

183. In the 1991/1992 season Hull City under the management of Terry Dolan finished 14th in which Division?

184. In November 1991 which player did Hull sell to Middlesbrough for £750,000?

185. Which team did Hull beat 8-4 in a 1996 FA Cup 1st round replay, with Duane Darby scoring a double hat-trick?

186. Who was the Tigers' top scorer for three consecutive seasons from 1994 to 1996 with a total of 44 League goals?

187. In Division Two in the 1994/1995 season, which team did Hull beat 7-1 at home on 29 October 1994?

188. In the 1990s Hull reached the FA Cup 3rd round on four occasions. Against which team did they draw twice in 1992 and again in 1999?

189. In the 1995/1996 season Hull finished bottom of the Division Two table with 31 points. How many League games did they win all season?

190. At the beginning of the 1996/1997 season Hull went how many League games before they were finally beaten?

2006/2007

191.   What award did the KC Stadium receive in 2006?

192.   Phil Parkinson was confirmed as Hull City's new
        manager on 29 June 2006, but from which club did he
        join the Tigers?

193.   Who was City's top League goalscorer with eight goals?

194.   Who played in all 46 of Hull's League games?

195.   Who was the Tigers' Player of the Season?

196.   Who scored the goal in a 1-0 away win at Cardiff City
        on 28 April 2007 to secure Hull's Championship status?

197.   Michael Bridges joined Hull from Carlisle United on 31
        August 2006, for what transfer fee?

198.   In what position did Hull City finish in the League?

199.   How many of the 46 League games did Hull win?

200.   On 30 January 2007 Hull recorded their highest gate
        attendance of 24,311, against which team?

KEN WAGSTAFF

201. Ken was born on 24 November in what year – 1940, 1942 or 1944?

202. Which manager signed Ken to play for Mansfield Town in 1960?

203. On 30 August 1960 Ken scored a brace on his League debut for Mansfield Town in a 2-1 win against which club?

204. What was Ken's nickname during his playing days?

205. Ken was transferred to Hull City on 12 November 1964, for what fee?

206. Ken scored on his debut for the Tigers in a win against Exeter City, but what was the final result – 3-1, 2-1 or 1-0?

207. How many League appearances did Ken make for the Tigers – 358, 368 or 378?

208. How many goals in all competitions did Ken score during his Hull City career?

209. In March 2005 what honour did Ken receive from the Hull City supporters?

210. How many different clubs did Ken play for during his 15-year professional career?

NATIONALITIES – 2

Match up the players and managers with their nationality

211.	Bernard Mendy	Trinidad and Tobago
212.	Nicky Featherstone	Hungarian
213.	Antonio Doncel	English
214.	Bobby Collins	Jamaican
215.	Jan Molby	French
216.	Ian Goodison	English
217.	Clint Marcelle	Scottish
218.	Peter Halmosi	English
219.	Ray Parlour	Danish
220.	Anthony Gardner	Spanish

1980s

221. How many League goals did Keith Edwards score for Hull in the 1988/1989 season?

222. What happened to Hull City Football Club in February 1982?

223. Who managed the Tigers from June 1982 to May 1984, winning 51% of his games while in charge?

224. On 29 January 1983 which team did Hull beat 7-0 at home in Division Four to record the season's highest team score?

225. In the 1981/1982 season Hull played Rochdale in the FA Cup 1st round, drawing 2-2 at home and then 2-2 away in the replay. Hull then won the second replay 1-0, but at which ground?

226. Hull finished runners-up to which team in Division Four in the 1982/1983 season?

227. In May 1985 which manager took Hull to promotion back into the Second Division?

228. In the 1987/1988 season which ex-Leeds United and Scotland player was appointed manager of Hull City?

229. Which chairman of Hull resigned in October 1989 after a home defeat to Brighton & Hove Albion?

230. In the summer of 1988 which team did Hull's goal keeper Tony Norman join?

DEAN WINDASS

231. In what year was Dean born – 1967, 1969 or 1971?

232. In what position does Dean play?

233. In what year did Dean sign for Hull City (first spell)?

234. Dean left Hull City in November 1995 and joined which Scottish team?

235. Dean returned to the Tigers in January 2007 whilst on loan from which Yorkshire team?

236. Following on from the previous question, Dean made 18 League appearances, scoring how many goals?

237. Hull paid £150,000 for Dean's services in 2007, but which manager signed him?

238. How many League goals did Dean score during 2007/2008, having made 37 appearances?

239. For which Premier League team did Dean play between 2001 and 2003?

240. Against which team did Dean score the third goal in a 3-1 away win during April 2008?

TERRY DOLAN

241. Terry was born on 11 June in which year – 1950, 1952 or 1954?

242. Where was Terry born – Barnsley, Bradford or Bingley?

243. In December 1969 which club did Terry sign for as a professional?

244. In October 1970 Terry signed for which club for the fee of £7,000, a club that he went on to play for in all four Divisions?

245. In January 1987 Terry became manager of Bradford City, but which manager did he replace there?

246. Which manager did Terry take over from at Hull in January 1991?

247. How many League and Cup games did Terry play during his 12-year professional career – 438, 448 or 458?

248. True or false: Terry played at all 92 League grounds?

249. At which club did Terry finish his playing career in 1981?

250. Which non-League club did Terry manage between October 2006 and November 2007?

NICK BARMBY

251. In what year was Nick born – 1972, 1974 or 1976?

252. Nick won 23 caps for England, his first cap being in 1995, but in what year was his last?

253. For which London club did Nick play between 1991 and 1995?

254. In what year did Nick sign for the Tigers?

255. Which City manager signed Nick for Hull?

256. How many promotions has Nick been involved with whilst at Hull City?

257. Nick made his City debut in a 1-0 home win against which team?

258. Against which team did Nick score his first Hull League goal, in a 3-2 away defeat?

259. Against which team did Nick score Hull's equaliser in a 1-1 away League draw during August 2007?

260. True or false: Nick scored in both of the matches in the Championship play-off semi-finals during May 2008 against Watford?

WHERE DID THEY GO? – 1

*Match up the player with the team he joined
on leaving Hull City*

261.	Andrew Brown	Brighton & Hove Albion
262.	Ben Wilkinson	Doncaster Rovers
263.	Ian McParland	Blackpool
264.	David Lill	Bridlington Town
265.	Scott Maxfield	York City
266.	Stephen Brentano	Doncaster Rovers
267.	Dave Livermore	Frickley Athletic
268.	Stuart Elliott	Dunfermline
269.	Malcolm Shotton	Rotherham United
270.	Steve McPhee	Clydebank

BRIAN LITTLE

271. In what year did Brian take over as Tigers manager?

272. Which Midlands club did Brian manage between 1994 and 1998?

273. How many England caps did Brian win as a player – 1, 11 or 21?

274. In what year was Brian born – 1951, 1953 or 1955?

275. When Brian took over at Hull, which club had he been managing earlier in that season?

276. Brian guided Hull City to the Division Three play-off final in 2001, only to be beaten by which club?

277. Brian managed Hull for 97 League games, but how many did they win – 41, 51 or 61?

278. True or false: Brian won promotion with Hull City in his first full season in charge?

279. Brian played for only one club during his playing days, which one?

280. In what year did Brian leave as Hull manager?

2003/2004

281. Who finished as Hull City's top League scorer with 18 goals?

282. Damien Delaney played in how many of the Tigers' 46 League appearances?

283. Hull's highest League attendance of 23,495 was on 24 April 2004, against which team?

284. On 6 May 2003 Hull City signed Danny Allsopp from Notts County, for what transfer fee?

285. Who was Hull City's Player of the Season?

286. In what position in the League did City finish, with 88 points?

287. How many of their 46 League games did City win – 20, 25 or 30?

288. Can you name the manager who was in charge of Hull City for this season?

289. What was the significance of Hull's 2-1 away win at Yeovil Town on 1 May 2004?

290. Jon Walters was sold for £50,000 on 3 February 2004 to which Premiership club?

1970s

291. On 1 August 1970 which team knocked Hull City out of the Watney Mann Invitation Cup on penalties?

292. From 1972 to 1974 who was Hull's top League goalscorer in three consecutive seasons with a total of 43 League goals?

293. In the 1970/1971 season, by which team were Hull beaten 2-3 in the 6th round of the FA Cup after leading the match 2-0?

294. Who replaced John Kaye as Hull manager in September 1977, remaining in that post until February 1978?

295. Who was dismissed as Hull's chief scout in December 1979?

296. In September 1979 Hull signed midfielder Mick Tait for £150,000 from which club?

297. In the 1970/1971 season of Division Two Hull were joint top with a highest aggregate score of eight when they drew 4-4 with which team on 26 December 1970?

298. Who was Hull's top League goalscorer in the 1970/1971 season, with 21 goals?

299. In what position did City finish in the League in the 1970/1971 season, with 51 points?

300. Who knocked Hull out of the 4th round of the FA Cup in the 1976/1976 season, beating them 1-0?

WHERE DID THEY COME FROM? – 2

Match up the player with the club from which he joined Hull City

301.	Dennis Burnett	Southend United
302.	Simon Trevitt	Grantham Town
303.	Jackie Sewell	Glasgow Rangers
304.	Peter Halmosi	Ipswich Town
305.	Frank Banks	Huddersfield Town
306.	Neil Mann	Aston Villa
307.	Neil Williams	Plymouth Argyle
308.	Dale Roberts	Paris Saint-Germain
309.	Bernard Mendy	Watford
310.	Brian McGinty	Millwall

PETER TAYLOR

311. In which Essex seaside resort was Peter born?

312. For which club did Peter start his professional football career in 1970?

313. Peter was playing for Crystal Palace when he made his England debut in 1975, but which Division were Palace in at the time?

314. How many appearances did Peter make for England at international level, scoring two goals?

315. In November 2002 Peter became manager of Hull City and subsequently won which two honours with the Tigers?

316. At which non-League club did Peter start his managerial career in 1986?

317. Can you name the two clubs for which Peter made over 100 appearances during his playing career?

318. How many League appearances did Peter make as a player, scoring 87 League goals – 378, 388 or 398?

319. Which Under-21 international team did Peter manage from 2004 to 2007?

320. In what position did Peter play?

KEN HOUGHTON

321. Ken was born on 18 October in which year – 1935, 1937 or 1939?

322. Which manager signed Ken to play for Hull City in the 1964/1965 season?

323. From which club did Ken sign to join Hull City?

324. How many League appearances did Ken make for the Tigers – 264, 274 or 284?

325. How many League goals did Ken score for Hull City – 59, 69 or 79?

326. After playing for Hull City for nine years Ken left in June 1973 to join which club?

327. Ken won a League Cup runners-up medal in 1961 in a 3-2 defeat on aggregate in the final against Aston Villa when playing for which team?

328. Ken finished his playing career at which non-League club?

329. In what position did Ken play?

330. Where was Ken born – Bradford, Rotherham or Sheffield?

CLIFF BRITTON

331. Cliff was born on 29 August in which year – 1909, 1911 or 1913?

332. With which team did Cliff win the FA Cup in 1933?

333. Cliff became Hull manager in July 1961 and his first match in charge was a 2-3 away win on 19 August 1961 against which team?

334. Cliff played at international level for England between 1934 and 1937, making how many appearances for his country?

335. At which West Country club did Cliff begin his professional playing career in August 1928?

336. Besides Hull, can you name the other three clubs that Cliff managed?

337. Cliff only played professionally for two clubs during his career. Can you name both of them?

338. Which other two players made England's halfback line-up along with Cliff?

339. In what position did Cliff play?

340. Which teammate at Everton made this following statement about Cliff: "He was the best crosser of the ball that I ever played with"?

2004/2005

341. Who finished as Hull's highest scorer with 27 League goals?

342. On 9 July 2004 which player was signed from Stockport County for £100,000?

343. Local boy Nick Barmby joined Hull on a free transfer on 8 July 2004, from which club?

344. How many of the 46 League games did Hull City win?

345. The Tigers went out of the FA Cup in the 3rd round at home, losing 0-2 to which team?

346. In what position in the League did Hull City finish?

347. Who was Hull's Player of the Season?

348. Who had the most League goal assists, with six?

349. The highest gate attendance of the season was 24,277 on 30 April 2005, when Hull played which opponents?

350. Who was the season's consistent left back for the Tigers?

LEAGUE GOALSCORERS – 2

*Match up the player with the total number of
League goals scored for the club*

351.	**Greg Rioch**	47
352.	**Alf Ackerman**	66
353.	**Tommy Martin**	8
354.	**Johnny Linaker**	49
355.	**Ian Butcher**	6
356.	**Garreth Roberts**	11
357.	**Bill Bradbury**	2
358.	**Wayne Jacobs**	3
359.	**Phil Holme**	82
360.	**Paul Haigh**	4

POSITIONS IN THE LEAGUE – 2

*Match up the season with the position in which
Hull City finished in the League*

361.	1987/1988	20th in Division Three
362.	1985/1986	22nd in Division Two
363.	1983/1984	6th in Division Two
364.	1981/1982	9th in Division Two
365.	1979/1980	12th in Division Two
366.	1977/1978	13th in Division Two
367.	1975/1976	15th in Division Two
368.	1973/1974	8th in Division Four
369.	1971/1972	4th in Division Three
370.	1969/1970	14th in Division Two

BRIAN HORTON

371.   In which Staffordshire town was Brian born?

372.   At which club did Brian start his professional playing
        career in 1970, making 236 League appearances for
        them and scoring 33 League goals?

373.   What fee did Brighton & Hove Albion pay Port Vale for
        Brian in 1976?

374.   Brian was playing for which team when they escaped
        relegation on the last day of the season in 1983 at
        Manchester City, thus relegating Manchester City to
        Division Two?

375.   How many League appearances did Brian make for the
        Tigers – 28, 38 or 48?

376.   Whom did Brian replace as manager of Hull City in
        June 1984?

377.   Brian was in charge of which non-League club when he
        achieved his 1,000th game as a manager in 2004?

378.   Brian went on to manage three of the four League
        clubs he played for. Can you name them?

379.   In what position did Brian play?

380.   During his 16-year playing career how many League
        appearances did Brian make – 410, 510 or 610?

2005/2006

381. Who was signed for £200,000 from Bristol City on 26 July 2005?

382. How many of the 46 League games did Hull City win?

383. Who started the season as captain but only played six games before a knee problem kept him off the pitch for the remainder of the season?

384. In November 2005 Billy Painter and Sam Collins came to Hull on loan from which club?

385. Which player made 45 League starts and one as substitute?

386. On 9 November 2005 Paul Anderson went to which club for work experience?

387. What was Hull's average attendance - 17,841, 18,841 or 19,841?

388. Who was the Tigers' top League goalscorer with seven goals?

389. Who was Hull City's Player of the Season?

390. In what position did City finish in the League, with 52 points?

TRANSFER FEES

Match up the player with his transfer fee

391.	George Boateng	Free Transfer from Scunthorpe United
392.	Alton Thelwell	Hull paid Leicester £250,000
393.	Michael Bridges	Hull paid Tottenham £2.5 million
394.	Craig Fagan	Wigan Athletic paid Hull £350,000
395.	Lawrie Dudfield	Leyton Orient paid Hull £25,000
396.	Andy Dawson	Brighton paid Hull £75,000
397.	Stuart Green	Hull paid Carlisle United £350,000
398.	Roy Carroll	Hull paid Middlesbrough £1 million
399.	Nicky Forster	Crystal Palace paid Hull £75,000
400.	Anthony Gardner	Hull paid Derby County £750,000

BRIAN MARWOOD

401. Brian was born on 2 February in which year – 1958, 1960 or 1962?

402. Which club did Brian join as an apprentice in 1976?

403. Brian made his Hull City debut at the age of 19 in a Third Division match against which team?

404. In his five years with the Tigers Brian scored 51 League goals, but how many League appearances did he make?

405. Which club signed Brian for £800,000 in May 1988?

406. Brian won the First Division Championship with which club in 1989?

407. Brian gained his only England cap on 16 November 1988 in a 1-1 away friendly against which international team?

408. Brian was chairman of which association between 1990 and 1993?

409. At which club did Brian finish his professional playing career in 1994?

410. True or false: Brian played for both Sheffield Wednesday and Sheffield United during his career?

TONY NORMAN

411. Tony was born on 24 February in which year – 1958,
       1960 or 1962?

412. Which club did Tony join in 1976, never playing a
       competitive League or Cup game for them during the
       following four years?

413. How many League appearances did Tony make for the
       Tigers?

414. Where was Tony born – Didcot, Ashcott or Mancot?

415. Between August 1983 and September 1988 how many
       consecutive appearances did Tony make for Hull City –
       226, 246 or 266?

416.   Tony made five appearances at international level for
       Wales usually serving at deputy to which legendary
       goalkeeper?

417. Which club did Tony join in 1988, making 198 League
       appearances for them and playing in the 1992 FA Cup
       final against Liverpool when Hull lost 2-0?

418. In 1995 Tony signed for Huddersfield Town. Which
       former Hull City manager was in charge at
       Huddersfield at the time?

419. At which club did Tony finish his professional playing
       career, making only seven League appearances for
       them?

420. Which occupation did Tony take up after retiring from
       football in 1998?

CHRIS CHILTON

421. Chris was born in Sproatley on 25 June in which year –
1941, 1943 or 1945?

422. What is the title of Chris's autobiography, published in
2005?

423. At which non-League club did Chris play as an amateur
before signing for Hull City in August 1958?

424. Chris made his Hull debut on 20 August 1960 in a 4-0
away win at which club?

425. How many League appearances did Chris make for the
Tigers – 415, 425 or 435?

426. Who was Chris's main striking partner at Hull City, with
whom he was joint-top League goalscorer in the
1969-70 season with 18 goals?

427. How many career hat-tricks did Chris score – 4, 8 or
12?

428. How many League goals did Chris score for Hull City
between 1960 and 1972?

429. Which club did Chris join from Hull in 1972 for
£90,000?

430. Chris finished his playing career at Highland Park, but
in which country is this club located?

LEAGUE APPEARANCES – 2

Match up the player with the number of League appearances he made for the club

431.	Billy Wilkinson	77 (27)
432.	Ian Wright	140 (10)
433.	David Walmsley	271 (27)
434.	Dale Roberts	65 (8)
435.	Andy Saville	208 (15)
436.	Stan McEwan	92 (8)
437.	David Mail	149 (4)
438.	Russell Wilcox	5 (5)
439.	Malcolm Lord	104 (12)
440.	Chris Lee	113

DEBUTS

*Match the player with the club against which he made his
League debut for Hull City on the given date*

441. Cliff Woodhead

Rotherham United
1 April 1939

442. Brian Marwood

Barnsley
2 September 1905

443. George Maddison

Colchester United
20 August 1960

444. Gordon Wright

Southport
20 December 1930

445. Matt Bell

Bury
15 October 1955

446. Billy Bly

West Bromwich Albion
7 April 1906

447. Bill Bradbury

Mansfield Town
12 January 1980

448. Raich Carter

Stoke City
8 September 1919

449. Martin Spendiff

Stockport County
8 November 1924

450. Chris Chilton

York City
3 April 1948

2007/2008

451.   Hull City went out of the League Cup in the 4th round, losing 4-0 away against which team?

452.   Who was the top League goalscorer with 15 goals?

453.   Caleb Folan was signed for the Tigers for £1 million on 31 August 2007, from which Premiership club?

454.   Damien Delaney left Hull on 17 January 2008 to join which London club?

455.   Who was the Player of the Season?

456.   In what position did Hull City finish in the League?

457.   What was the aggregate score over two legs when Hull City played Watford in the play-off semi-final?

458.   How many of the 46 League games did Hull win?

459.   With how many points did Hull finish the season?

460.   Who made 44 League appearances for the Tigers?

HAT-TRICKS

*Match up the fixture with the player that scored
a hat-trick for Hull City*

461. *v. Crewe Alexandra, Home, 7-1,
     October 1994, Division Two*   **Stuart Elliott**

462. *v. Bournemouth, Home, 4-0,
     August 1989, Division Two*   **Duane Darby**

463. *v. Southend United, Home, 4-0,
     March 2007, The Championship*   **Keith Edwards**

464. *v. Cambridge United, Away, 4-3,
     August 1993, Division Two*   **Keith Edwards**

465. *v. Chester City, Home, 3-0,
     September 1978, Division Three*   **Andy Payton**

466. *v. Darlington, Home, 3-2,
     August 1996, Division Three*   **Dean Windass**

467. *v. Tranmere Rovers, Home, 6-1,
     December 2004, League One*   **Dean Windass**

468. *v. Barnet, Home, 4-4,
     December 1993, Division Two*   **Linton Brown**

469. *v. Bournemouth, Home, 4-0,
     January 1989, Division Two*   **Ken Houghton**

470. *v. Birmingham City, Away, 4-2,
     April 1970, Division Two*   **Dean Windass**

KEITH EDWARDS

471. Keith was born in Stockton-on-Tees on 16 July in which year – 1953, 1955 or 1957?

472. Hull signed Keith from which club in August 1978 for £50,000?

473. Keith had two spells at Hull - 1978-81 and 1988-89 - but can you name the other club he had two spells with during his career?

474. Keith made his home debut for Hull City on 19 August 1978 in a 1-1 home draw against which team?

475. How many League appearances did Keith make for the Tigers – 185 (2), 190 (2) or 195 (2)?

476. How many League goals did Keith score while at Hull City – 76, 86 or 96?

477. After his second spell at Hull which team did Keith join in September 1989?

478. For which Scottish club did Keith play in 1987-88, making only nine League appearances for them and scoring two League goals?

479. Which Sheffield United manager paid £100,000 for Keith in September 1981?

480. At which club did Keith finish his professional career in 1991?

MATCH THE YEAR – 2

Match up the event with the correct year

481.	Hull were champions of Division Three North	1930
482.	Hull won promotion to the Premier League for the first time	1955
483.	John Kaye was appointed Hull City manager	1924
484.	George Maddison joined the Tigers from Spurs	2008
485.	Hull achieved their record win, 11-1 against Carlisle United	1933
486.	Craig Fagan joined Hull from Derby County,his second spell at the club	1949
487.	Hull were champions of Division Three North	1988
488.	Hull made it to the FA Cup semi-finals	1974
489.	Brian Horton left as Hull manager	1939
490.	Bill Bradbury signed for the Tigers from Birmingham City	2008

PHIL BROWN

491.   Phil was born on 30 May in which year – 1957, 1959 or 1961?

492.   In 1978-88 Phil played alongside which fellow north-easterner at Hartlepool United and Halifax Town, also playing under him at Halifax?

493.   How many League appearances did Phil make during his career – 632, 652 or 672?

494.   In what position did Phil play?

495.   At which club did Phil serve as caretaker manager in 1999?

496.   Whom did Phil succeed as manager of Derby County in June 2005?

497.   Phil was appointed as first team coach for Hull City on 27 October 2006, but who was the manager at that time?

498.   Where was Phil born – North Shields, Gateshead or South Shields?

499.   At which club did Phil end his playing career in 1996, making 44 League appearances for them and scoring five League goals?

500.   In May 2008 what did Phil describe as "the best day of my life, without a shadow of a doubt"?

WINNING GOALS

Match the fixture with the player that scored
Hull's winning goal

501. *v. Plymouth Argyle, The Championship*
     February 2008, 1-0   **Ian Ashbee**

502. *v. Fulham, Home, Premier League,*
     August 2008, 2-1   **Stuart Elliott**

503. *v. Darlington, Home, League Two,*   **Duane Darby**
     August 1996, 3-2

504. *v. Bristol City, Wembley, Play-off Final,*
     May 2008, 1-0   **Stuart Elliott**

505. *v. Crystal Palace, The Championship,*
     April 2008, 2-1   **Andy Holt**

506. *v. Wigan Athletic, Away, League Cup,*
     August 2007, 1-0   **Dean Windass**

507. *v. Crystal Palace, Home, League Cup,*
     September 1997, 2-1   **Ian Ashbee**

508. *v. Boston United, Away, League Two,*
     April 2003, 1-0   **Dean Windass**

509. *v. Scunthorpe United, Home, League Two,*
     April 2001, 2-1   **Duane Darby**

510. *v. Yeovil Town, Away, League Two,*
     May 2004, 2-1   **Caleb Folan**

STUART PEARSON

511. Stuart was born on 21 June 1949 in which city?

512. Stuart started his professional career at Hull City and made his debut on 15 April 1970 in a home 3-3 draw against which team?

513. What was Stuart's nickname during his playing days?

514. In 1974 Stuart was signed by which club for £200,000 after they were relegated to Division Two?

515. How many League appearances did Stuart make for the Tigers – 126 (3), 136 (3) or 146 (3)?

516. At which club did Stuart serve as coach in 1985-86?

517. Stuart played at international level for England, making 13 (2) appearances, but how many goals did he score?

518. With which club did Stuart win the FA Cup in 1980?

519. In what year did Stuart retire from League football due to a knee injury?

520. How many League goals did Stuart score for the Tigers?

ANDY DAVIDSON

521. Andy was born in Douglas Water, Scotland, on 13 July of which year – 1930, 1932 or 1934?

522. Andy made his Hull debut on 8 September 1952 in a 2-0 away win at which club?

523. In what position did Andy play at Hull City?

524. In 1968 a Scottish club took an interest in Andy, but he turned them down – which club?

525. How many League appearances did Andy make for the Tigers?

526. Which honour did Andy win with Hull City in the 1960s?

527. Which Scottish team did Andy support as a boy?

528. How many League goals did Andy score for the Tigers – 18, 24 or 30?

529. What was Andy's nickname during his Hull City playing days?

530. During his 16-year Hull City playing career Andy broke his leg on how many occasions, each time fighting back to full fitness?

POSITIONS IN THE LEAGUE – 3

Match up the season with the position in which
Hull City finished in the League

531.	1967/1968	22nd in Division Two
532.	1965/1966	5th in Division Three North
533.	1963/1964	1st in Division Three
534.	1961/1962	7th in Division Two
535.	1959/1960	17th in Division Two
536.	1957/1958	10th in Division Three
537.	1955/1956	15th in Division Two
538.	1953/1954	21st in Division Two
539.	1951/1952	8th in Division Three
540.	1949/1950	18th in Division Two

GARRETH ROBERTS

541. Garreth was born on 15 November 1960 in which north-east city?

542. Garreth made his Hull City debut as a substitute on 10 March 1979 in a 4-1 home win against which team?

543. How many League appearances did Garreth make for the Tigers – 409 (5), 419 (5) or 429 (5)?

544. In what positions did Garreth play at Hull City?

545. At which club did Garreth sign as an apprentice in January 1978?

546. How many League goals did Garreth score for Hull City – 27, 37 or 47?

547. On which radio station does Garreth appear regularly during commentary on live Hull City matches?

548. For which other club did Garreth play during his professional career?

549. Garreth scored 59 goals in all competitions for Hull City, making how many appearances?

550. In what year did Garreth retire from playing football?

2002/2003

551.　Who was the top League goalscorer, with 12 goals?

552.　When completed in 2002 how much did the KC Stadium complex cost?

553.　Which former Liverpool player was manager at Hull from April to October 2002?

554.　On 18 December 2002 the Tigers played their first match against Sunderland at the KC Stadium and won the Raich Carter Trophy by winning 1-0 in front of a crowd of 22,467, but who scored that very first goal?

555.　In what position in the League did City finish, with 59 points?

556.　Which team did Hull beat 4-1 in their last home game on 26 April 2003, with Ben Burgess scoring a hat-trick?

557.　Hull played 11 home games at Boothferry Park before moving to the new stadium, but how many home games did they play at the KC Stadium?

558.　The biggest home attendance was on 26 December 2002, with a crowd of 22,319 seeing Hull win 2-0 against which team?

559.　In an away match on 15 March 2003 at Rushden & Diamonds, which Hull player got sent off just before half-time in Hull's 4-2 defeat?

560.　On 1 March 2003 which team did Hull beat 5-1 away, with Walters and Elliott scoring a brace each and Forrester the other goal?

LEAGUE GOALSCORERS – 3

Match up the player with the total number of League goals scored for the club

561.	Darren France	6
562.	Duane Darby	44
563.	Doug Clarke	27
564.	Neil Allison	7
565.	Russell Wainscoat	51
566.	Stuart Pearson	7
567.	Dale Roberts	42
568.	Ian McParland	3
569.	Viggo Jensen	3
570.	Ray Daniel	79

LEAGUE ONE RUNNERS-UP – 2004/2005

571. Who was Hull's top scorer with 27 goals in 36 appearances?

572. True or false: Not one City player played in all 46 League games?

573. Which centre forward did Hull sign from Colchester United during February 2005?

574. Hull finished 12 points behind which team in League One?

575. Against which team did Hull record their biggest win of the season, a 6-1 home win during December 2004?

576. True or false: Hull won all 5 League games during December 2004?

577. Which midfielder signed for Hull City during January 2005 from Chester City?

578. True or false: Hull were beaten 2-1 by Brentford on the last day of the season?

579. Which team did Hull beat 2-0 away on Boxing Day 2004, with Stuart Elliott scoring a brace?

580. How many of their 46 League games did Hull win – 20, 23 or 26?

2001/2002

581.   In what position in the League did City finish, with 61 points?

582.   Who was the top league goalscorer with 17 goals?

583.   Which player did Hull sign from Leicester City for £250,000 on 22 June 2001?

584.   How many of the 46 League games did Gary Alexander play?

585.   Hull recorded their biggest win on 3 November 2001, a 5-1 home thrashing of which club?

586.   On 17 November 2001 which team did Hull City beat 5-2 away in the 1st round of the FA Cup?

587.   In which competition did Hull City beat Wrexham 3-2 away?

588.   Which team knocked Hull out of the Football League Trophy, beating them 1-0 at home on 8 January 2002?

589.   Matthew Wicks joined Hull and David Lee left Hull in a swap on 11 January 2002, with which club?

590.   Hull City only drew with one club, 0-0 at home and 1-1 away - which club?

AGAINST WHICH TEAM?

591. Hull played them in their first ever Premier League game in 2008.

592. Hull beat them 1-0 on the opening day of the 1992/1993 season.

593. Hull lost 5-4 to them in August 1989 in Division Two, with Andy Payton scoring a hat-trick.

594. Hull lost 2-1 to them in the Associate Members' Cup final during May 1984.

595. Hull beat them 6-1 in September 1966 at home in Division Two.

596. Syd Gerrie scored four goals against them in January 1952 in Division Two in a 5-0 home win.

597. Hull lost to them on the final day of the 2007/2008 League season.

598. Dave King scored a hat-trick against them during April 1962 in Division Three in a 4-0 home win.

599. Hull beat them 3-2 away from home during October 2006, with Jon Parkin, Stuart Elliott and Craig Fagan scoring.

600. Hull beat them 4-1 on the opening day of the season during August 2003.

WHERE DID THEY GO? – 2

*Match up the player with the team he joined
on leaving Hull City*

601.	John Bennion	Macclesfield Town
602.	Kenny Gilbert	York City
603.	Les Metrie	Grantham Town
604.	Alan Fettis	Manchester United
605.	Dean Keates	Wigan Athletic
606.	Simon Dakin	Chesterfield
607.	Colin Alcide	Colchester United
608.	Roy Carroll	Kidderminster
609.	Pat O'Connell	Ross County
610.	David D'Auria	Stockport County

DIVISION THREE RUNNERS-UP – 2003/2004

611.   Which club finished four points ahead of Hull and were crowned champions of Division Three?

612.   Can you name the other two clubs that won promotion?

613.   Who was the Tigers' manager during this season?

614.   Who finished as top League scorer, with 18 goals in 44 games?

615.   Following on from the previous question, Stuart Elliott also scored double figures in his 42 appearances, but how many goals?

616.   Who was the only player to play in all 46 League games, scoring two goals?

617.   Which team did Hull beat 4-1 on the opening day of the season?

618.   Against which club did City record their biggest win of the season, a 6-1 home win, with Ben Burgess scoring a brace?

619.   How many of their 46 League games did City win?

620.   Which team did Hull beat 3-0 on the last day of the season, with Jason Price, Damien Delaney and Stuart Elliott scoring?

DIVISION THREE PROMOTION – 1984/1985

621. In what position did Hull finish in the League?

622. True or false: The Tigers won all of their final three matches of the season during May 1985?

623. Who was Hull's top League scorer with 30 goals in 40 appearances?

624. Can you name the other two players that scored double figures in League matches?

625. Who was the manager of City during this season?

626. The highest League attendance was 15,795 on 6 May 1985, but which team were Hull playing that day?

627. Against which London team did Hull record their highest win of the season, a 5-1 victory, during April 1985?

628. Following on from the previous question, who scored a hat-trick in the game?

629. Which goalkeeper played in all 46 League games?

630. Following on from the previous question, which other two players played in all 46 League matches for the Tigers?

1960s

631. Who scored 27 League goals for Hull in the Division Three season of 1964/1965?

632. Who managed Hull from 1961 to 1969 and was in charge for 406 League games?

633. How much cash did the Hull chairman Harold Needler give to the club in 1963?

634. In the 1965/1966 season an attendance of 40,231 watched Hull's Division Three top-of-the-table clash against which team?

635. In what position did Hull City finish in the League in the 1965/1966 season, with 69 points?

636. Which team knocked Hull out of the FA Cup quarter-final, beating them 3-1 in a replay on 31 March 1966?

637. Which player was transferred to Tranmere Rovers on 1 March 1961 after spending two seasons with Hull City?

638. In 1966 which two teams did Hull City beat at home 6-1?

639. Which club knocked Hull City out of the League Cup, beating them 5-1 on 19 October 1960?

640. Which eventual winners of the 1969 FA Cup final knocked Hull out in Round 3, beating them 1-0?

DIVISION FOUR RUNNERS-UP – 1982/1983

641. Which City manager was in charge during this season, his first in charge?

642. Who was Hull's top League scorer, with 19 goals in 40 games?

643. Can you name the two other players that finished the season on double figures, one scoring 13 League goals and the other scoring 12?

644. Who was the only Tiger to play in every League match during this season?

645. Hull's first League win of the season came at the third attempt, in a 4-0 home win against which team?

646. Against which team did Hull record their biggest win of the season, a 7-0 home win during January 1983?

647. Following on from the previous question, who scored a hat-trick in the game?

648. True or false: Hull were unbeaten in the League during December 1982?

649. Can you name the two goalkeepers that played in the club's 46 League games during the season?

650. Who won the League title, with Hull finishing eight points behind them?

2000/2001

651.   In what position did Hull City finish in the League?

652.   Who was the top League goalscorer, with five goals?

653.   What happened at Boothferry Park in May 2000, resulting in Hull City being unable to play a game there?

654.   In the Division Three play-off semi-final which team beat Hull City 2-1 on aggregate?

655.   Which Hull player made the most League appearances of 40 (2)?

656.   Kevin Francis signed for Hull City on a free transfer from which club?

657.   With which two clubs did Hull City draw 0-0 both home and away?

658.   Which player did Hull sign for £150,000 on 27 May 2001 from Oldham Athletic?

659.   Paul Musselwhite played 37 League games for Hull and received the yellow card just once, on 27 January 2001, against which team?

660.   Phil Brumwell, David Brightwell, Steve Harper and Clint Marcelle all left Hull to play for which club?

WHO AM I? - 2

661.   I am a centre forward from Brazil and I scored on my Premier League debut during August 2008 against Fulham.

662.   I signed from Spurs in July 2008, I am an England international and I started my career at Port Vale.

663.   I managed the Tigers between February 1923 and May 1931.

664.   I signed for City from Spurs in 1924 and made 430 League appearances for the club.

665.   I signed from Middlesbrough in 2008, and my past clubs include Feyenoord, Coventry and Aston Villa.

666.   I signed on my debut against Kidderminster Harriers in a 6-1 home win during 2003, I played in midfield and I was born in Sheffield.

667.   I signed from Rotherham United in 1964 and made 305 League appearances for the Tigers, scoring 66 goals.

668.   I was born in Halifax, I signed for City in 1993 from Scarborough and I made 116 League appearances, scoring five goals.

669.   I am a defender who signed from Brentford in 2006, and my first League goal was against Crystal Palace during September 2006.

670.   I managed Hull City between June 1988 and May 1989.

HONOURS

Match up the honour achieved with the correct year

671.	**Third Division Champions**	*2008*
672.	**Third Division North Champions**	*2004*
673.	**Fourth Division Runners-Up**	*2005*
674.	**League One Runners-Up**	*2008*
675.	**Third Division North Champions**	*1966*
676.	**Championship Play-Off Winners**	*1949*
677.	**Third Division Promotion**	*1959*
678.	**Won their first Premier League match**	*1933*
679.	**Third Division North Runners-Up**	*1985*
680.	**Division Three Runners-Up**	*1983*

BILLY ASKEW

681. Billy was born in Great Lumley, County Durham, in October of which year – 1955, 1957 or 1959?

682. In 1983 Hull won promotion from Division Four, coming second to Wimbledon, but how many League goals did Billy score in the 1982/1983 season?

683. From which club did Billy join Hull City in August 1982?

684. How many League goals did Billy score for the Tigers – 15, 19 or 23?

685. Which is the only season, out of the eight that Billy spent with Hull, in which he played all 46 League games?

686. Who was Billy's popular teammate at Hull City, known as Big Billy?

687. How many League appearances did Billy make for Hull City – 247 (6), 257 (6) or 267 (6)?

688. At which club did Billy start his career as an apprentice in 1977?

689. True or false: Billy scored only one FA Cup goal during his professional career?

690. Which club did Billy join in 1989, playing only five full games for them and one as a substitute?

ANDY FLOUNDERS

691.   Where was Andy born – Hull, Selby or York?

692.   Which club did Andy join as an apprentice in 1978?

693.   On 29 January 1983 Hull City beat Stockport County
        7-0 at Boothferry Park, but how many of the seven
        goals did Andy score?

694.   How many League appearances did Andy make for
        Hull City – 116 (33), 126 (33) or 136 (33)?

695.   With which non-League club did Andy win the FA Vase
        at Wembley in 1996?

696.   On 4 March 1986 Andy hit a hat-trick in a 4-3 home
        win in Division Two against which team?

697.   How many League goals did Andy score for the Tigers
        – 34, 44 or 54?

698.   When Andy left Hull City in 1987 which club did he
        join?

699.   In a professional career spanning 15 years Andy made
        494 (61) appearances in all competitions, scoring how
        many goals?

700.   At which club did Andy finish his playing career in
        1995?

POSITIONS THEY PLAYED

Match the player with the position he played in for Hull City

701.   Cliff Woodhead   Goalkeeper

702.   Bill McNaughton   Midfield

703.   Douglas Duncan   Forward

704.   Ken Houghton   Left back

705.   George Maddison   Fullback

706.   Thomas Bleakley   Goalkeeper

707.   Cliff Hubbard   Left half

708.   John McQuillan   Fullback

709.   Matt Bell   Centre Forward

710.   Martin Spendiff   Outside left

LEAGUE APPEARANCES – 3

*Match up the player with the number of League
appearances he made for the club*

711.	Paul Hunter	1 (4)
712.	Steve Hoolickin	11 (8)
713.	Bobby McNeil	14 (12)
714.	Andy Mason	31
715.	Craig Lawford	121 (2)
716.	Tim Hotte	65
717.	Dennis Booth	135 (3)
718.	Dave King	45 (17)
719.	Duane Darby	37 (31)
720.	Stuart Young	79 (7)

RAICH CARTER

721. Raich was born in 1913 in which north-east city?

722. Raich made his Hull City debut on 3 April 1948 in a 1-1 home draw against which team?

723. From which club did Raich join Hull in March 1948?

724. Which two honours did Raich win as a player with Sunderland in 1936 and 1937?

725. How many England caps did Raich win at international level, including the wartime internationals – 25, 30 or 35?

726. How many League appearances did Raich make for the Tigers?

727. How many League goals did Raich score for Hull City – 37, 47 or 57?

728. Raich was manager of which team in 1956, taking them to promotion back to Division One?

729. What building opened in Sunderland in 2001 in honour of Raich?

730. True or false: Raich also played cricket for Derbyshire in 1946?

BOAZ MYHILL

731. Boaz was born on 9 November in which year – 1980, 1982 or 1984?

732. In what country was Boaz born?

733. At which club did Boaz start his professional football career in 2001?

734. In 2003 Boaz played 16 League games on loan for which team?

735. Which Hull manager brought Boaz to the KC Stadium in December 2003 for £50,000?

736. Boaz made his international debut for Wales on 26 March 2008, coming on as a half-time substitute in a 2-0 away win against which team?

737. For which club did Boaz make his first team debut on loan in November 2002, a game that saw Sheffield United put five past him?

738. True or false: Boaz was named the No. 1 keeper in 'FourFourTwo' magazine's list of the top-50 Football League players in 2006?

739. In the 2006/2007 season how many League and Cup games did Boaz play for Hull City?

740. On 12 February 2008 Boaz made his 200th appearance for Hull in a 1-1 away draw with which team?

WHERE DID THEY COME FROM? – 3

Match up the player with the club he signed from to join City

741.	Billy Askew	Stockton
742.	Mark Greaves	Middlesbrough
743.	Lee Warren	Derby County
744.	Mike Quigley	Gateshead
745.	Billy Wilkinson	Leeds United
746.	Craig Fagan	Rotherham
747.	Malcolm Shotton	Brigg Town
748.	George Boateng	Manchester City
749.	Mark Oxley	Barnsley
750.	Chris Galvin	Rochdale

BILLY BLY

751. Billy was born on 15 May in which year – 1920, 1922 or 1924?

752. Billy made his Hull City debut on 1 April 1939 away to which club?

753. Billy had a testimonial match at Hull against an All Star XI in October of which year?

754. How many League appearances did Billy make for the Tigers – 403, 413 or 423?

755. In what position did Billy play for Hull City?

756. Which honour did Billy win with Hull City in 1949?

757. How many FA Cup appearances did Billy make for the Tigers – 25, 30 or 35?

758. Billy joined Hull City in August 1937 from which club?

759. True or false: Billy played in the very first League match at Boothferry Park against Lincoln City, which ended 0-0?

760. Which non-League club did Billy join on a free transfer in August 1961?

SQUAD NUMBERS – 2008/2009 - 2

Match up the player with his squad number for the season

761.	Richard Garcia	18
762.	Nick Barmby	37
763.	Boaz Myhill	6
764.	George Boateng	4
765.	Dean Marney	1
766.	Caleb Folan	14
767.	Tony Warner	8
768.	Ian Ashbee	26
769.	Michael Turner	22
770.	Bill Law	20

WHERE DID THEY GO? – 3

*Match up the player with the team he joined
on leaving Hull City*

771.	Simon Trevitt	Nottingham Forest
772.	Frank Bunn	Crystal Palace
773.	Ken Knighton	Swansea City
774.	Darryl Duffy	Liverpool
775.	Andy Duncan	Sheffield Wednesday
776.	Mike Hollifield	Oldham Athletic
777.	Alan Fettis	Tottenham Hotspur
778.	Paul Anderson	Guiseley
779.	Leon Cort	Birmingham City
780.	Jeff Wealands	Tranmere Rovers

BIG WINS – 2

Match up the fixture with Hull's high-scoring victory

781.	v. Crewe Alexandra, Away, League Cup, August 2007	4-1
782.	v. Tranmere Rovers, Home, League, December 2004	8-4
783.	Northwich, Away, FA Cup, November 2001	7-4
784.	v. Southend United, Home, League, March 2007	5-1
785.	v. Swansea City, Home, League, August 1997	5-2
786.	v. Whitby Town, Home, FA Cup, November 1996	6-1
787.	v. Southampton, Home, League, March 2008	7-1
788.	v. Darlington, Home, League, August 2003	5-0
789.	v. Cheltenham Town, Home, League, November 2001	4-0
790.	v. Crewe Alexandra, Home, League, October 1994	3-0

CRAIG FAGAN

791. In which Midlands City was Craig born?

792. Which club did Craig join for £750,000 in January 2007?

793. Which club did Craig join as a trainee in October 2002, playing one game as a substitute in December 2002 against Southampton in the Premiership?

794. Craig joined Hull City on 28 February 2005 for his first spell at the club, making how many League appearances?

795. How many League goals did Craig score in his first spell at Hull City – 10, 15 or 20?

796. Craig is eligible to play for England and which other country?

797. Which manager brought Craig to Hull City on 2 July 2008?

798. Following on from the above question, how much was the transfer fee?

799. At the end of the 2007/2008 season Craig had a loan spell with Hull City and made his second debut on 8 March 2008 in a 2-0 home win against which team?

800. Craig made an appearance as a 67th minute substitute in the play-off final against Bristol City at Wembley, but which player did he replace?

ANSWERS

HISTORY OF THE CLUB

1. 1904
2. Kingston Communication Stadium
3. Boothferry Park
4. The Tigers
5. 2008
6. Fulham
7. Black and amber
8. Roary the Tiger
9. Andy Davidson
10. Manchester United

NATIONALITIES – 1

11.	Boaz Myhill	Welsh
12.	Geovanni Deiberson	Brazilian
13.	Richard Garcia	Australian
14.	Nick Barmby	English
15.	Caleb Folan	Irish
16.	George Boateng	Dutch
17.	Sam Ricketts	Welsh
18.	Wayne Brown	English
19.	Liam Cooper	Scottish
20.	Tony Warner	Trinidad and Tobago

MANAGERS - 1

21.	Bob Brocklebank	1955-61
22.	Ambrose Langley	1905-13
23.	Terry Dolan	1991-97
24.	Ernest Blackburn	1936-46
25.	Terry Neill	1970-74
26.	Peter Taylor	2002-06
27.	Billy McCraken	1923-31
28.	Brian Horton	1984-88
29.	James Ramster	1904-05
30.	David Menzies	1916-21

SQUAD NUMBERS - 2008/2009 – 1

| 31. | Nathan Doyle | 2 |

32.	Ryan France	13
33.	Will Atkinson	31
34.	Bryan Hughes	11
35.	Tom Woodhead	43
36.	Andy Dawson	3
37.	Craig Fagan	7
38.	Matt Duke	12
39.	John Welsh	19
40.	Wayne Brown	5

WHERE DID THEY COME FROM? – 1

41.	Richard Jobson	Watford
42.	Geovanni Deiberson	Manchester City
43.	Mick Hollifield	Wolves
44.	Syd Gerrie	Dundee
45.	Derek Hood	West Bromwich Albion
46.	Bruce Bannister	Plymouth Argyle
47.	Kevin Gage	Preston North End
48.	Mark Hateley	Glasgow Rangers
49.	Alex Dyer	Blackpool
50.	Bob Dewhurst	Blackburn Rovers

TOP TEN LEAGUE APPEARANCES

51.	Tommy Bleakley	368
52.	George Maddison	430
53.	Ken Wagstaff	374 (4)
54.	Garreth Roberts	365 (5)
55.	Billy Bly	403
56.	Matt Bell	393
57.	Andy Davidson	520
58.	Tony Norman	372
59.	Doug Clarke	368
60.	Chris Chilton	415

INTERNATIONAL CAPS

61.	Brian Marwood	1 cap for England
62.	Theodore Whitmore	105 caps for Jamaica
63.	Jay-Jay Okocha	75 caps for Nigeria

64.	Tony Norman	5 caps for Wales
65.	Emlyn Hughes	62 caps for England
66.	Aidan Davidson	3 caps for Northern Ireland
67.	George Boateng	4 caps for Holland
68.	Billy Bremner	54 caps for Scotland
69.	Mark Hateley	32 caps for England
70.	Stan Mortensen	25 caps for England

LEAGUE APPEARANCES – 1

71.	Matt Bell	393
72.	Tony Brien	43 (4)
73.	Andy Flounders	126 (33)
74.	Dai Davies	141
75.	Stuart Croft	187 (3)
76.	Ken Houghton	253 (11)
77.	Gary Hobson	135 (7)
78.	Peter Skipper	286 (2)
79.	Ray Daniel	55 (3)
80.	Garreth Roberts	409 (5)

THE LEAGUE CUP

81. 5-4 (1-2 at home and 4-2 away)
82. Andy Payton
83. Arsenal
84. Crewe Alexandra
85. Michael Bridges, Richard Garcia and Steve McPhee
86. Frank Bunn
87. Wigan Athletic
88. Roy Greenwood
89. Stockport County
90. Ken Knighton

GOALKEEPERS

91.	Billy Bly	1939-61
92.	George Maddison	1924-38
93.	Tony Norman	1980-88
94.	Martin Spendiff	1905-08
95.	Eddie Blackburn	1974-80

96.	Paul Musselwhite	2000-04
97.	Jeff Wealands	1972-79
98.	Nick Hendry	1910-20
99.	Tommy Forgan	1949-54
100.	Alan Fettis	1991-96

POSITIONS IN THE LEAGUE – 1

101.	2007/2008	3rd in the Championship
102.	2005/2006	18th in the Championship
103.	2003/2004	2nd in League Two
104.	2001/2002	11th in Division Two
105.	1999/2000	14th in Division Two
106.	1997/1998	22nd in Division Three
107.	1995/1996	24th in Division Two
108.	1993/1994	9th in Division Two
109.	1991/1992	14th in Division Three
110.	1989/1990	14th in Division Two

THE CHAMPIONSHIP PLAY-OFF FINAL – 2008

111. 3rd

112. Watford

113. 4-1 to Hull City

114. Nick Barmby, Caleb Folan, Richard Garcia and Nathan Doyle

115. Phil Brown

116. Bristol City

117. 1-0 to Hull City

118. Dean Windass

119. 86,703

120. Boaz Myhill, Sam Ricketts, Wayne Brown, Michael Turner, Andy Dawson, Richard Garcia, Ian Ashbee, Bryan Hughes, Nick Barmby, Fraizer Campbell and Dean Windass

BIG WINS – 1

121.	v. Cardiff City, Home, League, February 1995	4-0
122.	v. Darlington, Home, League, October 1991	5-2

123.	v. Fulham, Home, League,	
	November 1985	5-0
124.	v. Shrewsbury Town, Home, League,	
	March 1986	4-3
125.	v. Rotherham United, Home, League,	
	November 1993	4-1
126.	v. Leicester City, Home, League,	
	November 1990	5-2
127.	v. Exeter City, Home, League,	
	April 1994	5-1
128.	v. Leyton Orient, Away, League,	
	November 1984	5-4
129.	v. Preston North End, Home, League,	
	January 1973	6-2
130.	v. Swansea City, Home, League,	
	May 1992	3-0

WHO AM I?

131.	Nicky Forster
132.	Stan Mortensen
133.	Mark Hateley
134.	Billy Bremner
135.	Ken Wagstaff
136.	Jackie Crawford
137.	Leon Cort
138.	Andy Payton
139.	Ray Parlour
140.	Dean Windass

MANAGERS – 2

141.	John Kaye	1974-77
142.	Stan Ternent	1989-91
143.	Fred Stringer	1914-16
144.	Bob Jackson	1952-55
145.	Cliff Britton	1961-69
146.	Brian Little	2000-02
147.	Haydn Green	1931-34
148.	Harry Chapman	1913-14

| 149. | Raich Carter | 1948-51 |
| 150. | Percy Lewis | 1921-23 |

LEAGUE GOALSCORERS – 1

151.	Ray Henderson	54
152.	Linton Brown	24
153.	Alan Jarvis	12
154.	Keith Edwards	86
155.	Mark Hateley	3
156.	Lee Warren	1
157.	Chris Chilton	193
158.	Ken Wagstaff	173
159.	Gary Swann	9
160.	Andy Davidson	18

THE FA CUP

161.	Duane Darby
162.	Morecambe (1st round) and Blackpool (2nd round)
163.	Dean Windass
164.	Keith Edwards
165.	Nicky Forster
166.	Andy Flounders
167.	West Ham United
168.	Cardiff City
169.	Chelsea
170.	5: Hull won after four replays

MATCH THE YEAR – 1

171.	The club was formed	1904
172.	Stan Ternent was born	1946
173.	Phil Brown took over as the Tigers' manager	2006
174.	Hull were champions of Division Three	1966
175.	Brian Horton took over as Hull manager	1984
176.	Terry Neill was born	1942
177.	Nick Barmby joined the Tigers	2004
178.	Mark Hateley took over as Hull manager	1997
179.	Bob Brocklebank left as Hull manager	1961

180.	Wayne Jacobs signed for Hull City from Sheffield Wednesday	1987

1990s

181. Mark Hateley
182. David Lloyd
183. The Third Division
184. Andy Payton
185. Whitby Town
186. Dean Windass
187. Crewe Alexandra
188. Chelsea
189. 5 (drew 16 and lost 25)
190. 10

2006/2007

191. The best ground in the Football League awards
192. Colchester United
193. Dean Windass
194. Boaz Myhill
195. Andy Davidson
196. Dean Windass
197. £325,000
198. 21st
199. 13
200. Leeds United

KEN WAGSTAFF

201. 1942
202. Raich Carter
203. Rochdale
204. Waggy
205. £40,000
206. 3-1
207. 378
208. 197
209. He was voted 'Tiger' of the 20th Century
210. 2 (Mansfield Town and Hull City)

NATIONALITIES – 2

211.	Bernard Mendy	French
212.	Nicky Featherstone	English
213.	Antonio Doncel	Spanish
214.	Bobby Collins	Scottish
215.	Jan Molby	Danish
216.	Ian Goodison	Jamaican
217.	Clint Marcelle	Trinidad and Tobago
218.	Peter Halmosi	Hungarian
219.	Ray Parlour	English
220.	Anthony Gardner	English

1980s

221. 26

222. Hull were placed into receivership

223. Colin Appleton

224. Stockport County

225. Elland Road, Leeds United

226. Wimbledon

227. Brian Horton

228. Eddie Gray

229. Don Robinson

230. Sunderland

DEAN WINDASS

231. 1969

232. Forward

233. 1991

234. Aberdeen

235. Bradford City

236. 8

237. Phil Brown

238. 11

239. Middlesbrough

240. Barnsley

TERRY DOLAN

241. 1950

242. Bradford
243. Bradford Park Avenue
244. Huddersfield Town
245. Trevor Cherry
246. Stan Ternent
247. 448
248. True
249. Rochdale
250. Guiseley

NICK BARMBY

251. 1974
252. 2001
253. Tottenham Hotspur
254. 2004
255. Peter Taylor
256. 2: 2004/2005 (League One) and 2007/2008 (Championship)
257. Bournemouth
258. Port Vale
259. Coventry City
260. True

WHERE DID THEY GO? – 1

261.	Andrew Brown	Clydebank
262.	Ben Wilkinson	York City
263.	Ian McParland	Dunfermline
264.	David Lill	Rotherham United
265.	Scott Maxfield	Doncaster Rovers
266.	Stephen Brentano	Bridlington Town
267.	Dave Livermore	Brighton & Hove Albion
268.	Stuart Elliott	Doncaster Rovers
269.	Malcolm Shotton	Frickley Athletic
270.	Steve McPhee	Blackpool

BRIAN LITTLE

271. 2000
272. Aston Villa
273. 1

274. 1953
275. West Bromwich Albion
276. Leyton Orient
277. 41
278. False
279. Aston Villa
280. 2002

2003/2004

281. Ben Burgess
282. All 46
283. Huddersfield Town
284. £90,000
285. Damien Delaney
286. 2nd
287. 25
288. Peter Taylor
289. Hull clinched promotion to Division Two
290. Bolton Wanderers

1970s

291. Manchester United
292. Stuart Pearson
293. Stoke City
294. Bobby Collins
295. Andy Davidson
296. Carlisle United
297. Sheffield Wednesday
298. Chris Chilton
299. 5th
300. Sunderland

WHERE DID THEY COME FROM? – 2

301.	Dennis Burnett	Millwall
302.	Simon Trevitt	Huddersfield Town
303.	Jackie Sewell	Aston Villa
304.	Peter Halmosi	Plymouth Argyle
305.	Frank Banks	Southend United

306.	Neil Mann	Grantham Town
307.	Neil Williams	Watford
308.	Dale Roberts	Ipswich Town
309.	Bernard Mendy	Paris Saint-Germain
310.	Brian McGinty	Glasgow Rangers

PETER TAYLOR

311. Southend-on-Sea
312. Southend United
313. The Third Division
314. 4
315. League Two runners-up in 2004 and League One runners-up in 2005
316. Dartford
317. Crystal Palace (1973-76, 122 appearances) and Tottenham Hotspur (1976-80, 123 appearances)
318. 388
319. The England Under-21 team
320. Winger

KEN HOUGHTON

321. 1939
322. Cliff Britton
323. Rotherham United
324. 264
325. 79
326. Scunthorpe United
327. Rotherham United
328. Bridlington Town
329. Midfielder
330. Rotherham

CLIFF BRITTON

331. 1909
332. Everton
333. Peterborough United
334. 9
335. Bristol Rovers

336.	Burnley, Everton and Preston North End
337.	Bristol Rovers and Everton
338.	Joe Mercer and Stan Cullis
339.	Right half
340.	Dixie Dean

2004/2005

341.	Stuart Elliott
342.	Aaron Wilbraham
343.	Leeds United
344.	26
345.	Colchester United
346.	2nd
347.	Stuart Elliott
348.	Nick Barmby
349.	Sheffield Wednesday
350.	Andy Davidson

LEAGUE GOALSCORERS – 2

351.	Greg Rioch	6
352.	Alf Ackerman	49
353.	Tommy Martin	2
354.	Johnny Linaker	3
355.	Ian Butcher	66
356.	Garreth Roberts	47
357.	Bill Bradbury	82
358.	Wayne Jacobs	4
359.	Phil Holme	11
360.	Paul Haigh	8

POSITIONS IN THE LEAGUE – 2

361.	1987/1988	15th in Division Two
362.	1985/1986	6th in Division Two
363.	1983/1984	4th in Division Three
364.	1981/1982	8th in Division Four
365.	1979/1980	20th in Division Three
366.	1977/1978	22nd in Division Two
367.	1975/1976	14th in Division Two

368.	1973/1974	9th in Division Two
369.	1971/1972	12th in Division Two
370.	1969/1970	13th in Division Two

BRIAN HORTON

371.	Hednesford
372.	Port Vale
373.	£30,000
374.	Luton Town
375.	38
376.	Colin Appleton
377.	Alfreton Town
378.	Port Vale, Brighton & Hove Albion and Hull City. He did not manage Luton Town
379.	Midfielder
380.	610

2005/2006

381.	Danny Coles
382.	12
383.	Ian Ashbee
384.	Port Vale
385.	Damien Delaney
386.	Liverpool
387.	19,841
388.	Stuart Elliott
389.	Boaz Myhill
390.	18th

TRANSFER FEES

391.	George Boateng	Hull paid Middlesbrough £1 million
392.	Alton Thelwell	Leyton Orient paid Hull £25,000
393.	Michael Bridges	Hull paid Carlisle United £350,000
394.	Craig Fagan	Hull paid Derby County £750,000
395.	Lawrie Dudfield	Hull paid Leicester £250,000
396.	Andy Dawson	Free Transfer from Scunthorpe United
397.	Stuart Green	Crystal Palace paid Hull £75,000

398.	Roy Carroll	Wigan Athletic paid Hull £350,000
399.	Nicky Forster	Brighton paid Hull £75,000
400.	Anthony Gardner	Hull paid Tottenham £2.5 million

BRIAN MARWOOD

401.	1960
402.	Hull City
403.	Mansfield Town
404.	158
405.	Arsenal
406.	Arsenal
407.	Saudi Arabia
408.	The Professional Footballers' Association
409.	Barnet
410.	True: Sheffield Wednesday 1984-88 and Sheffield United 1990-92

TONY NORMAN

411.	1958
412.	Burnley
413.	372
414.	Mancot, Wales
415.	226
416.	Neville Southall
417.	Sunderland
418.	Brian Horton
419.	Huddersfield Town
420.	Policeman

CHRIS CHILTON

421.	1943
422.	Chillo
423.	Bilton FC
424.	Colchester United
425.	415
426.	Ken Wagstaff
427.	12
428.	193

429.	Coventry City
430.	South Africa

LEAGUE APPEARANCES – 2

431.	Billy Wilkinson	208 (15)
432.	Ian Wright	65 (8)
433.	David Walmsley	5 (5)
434.	Dale Roberts	149 (4)
435.	Andy Saville	77 (27)
436.	Stan McEwan	113
437.	David Mail	140 (10)
438.	Russell Wilcox	92 (8)
439.	Malcolm Lord	271 (27)
440.	Chris Lee	104 (12)

DEBUTS

441.	Cliff Woodhead	Southport - 20 December 1930
442.	Brian Marwood	Mansfield Town - 12 January 1980
443.	George Maddison	Stockport County - 8 November 1924
444.	Gordon Wright	West Bromwich Albion - 7 April 1906
445.	Matt Bell	Stoke City - 8 September 1919
446.	Billy Bly	Rotherham United - 1 April 1939
447.	Bill Bradbury	Bury - 15 October 1955
448.	Raich Carter	York City - 3 April 1948
449.	Martin Spendiff	Barnsley - 2 September 1905
450.	Chris Chilton	Colchester United - 20 August 1960

2007/2008

451.	Chelsea
452.	Fraizer Campbell
453.	Wigan Athletic
454.	Queens Park Rangers
455.	Michael Turner
456.	3rd
457.	Hull City 6, Watford 1 (1st leg, Watford 0, Hull 2; (2nd leg, Hull 4, Watford 1)
458.	21
459.	75

460.   Michael Turner

HAT-TRICKS

461.   v. Crewe Alexandra, Home, 7-1,
        October 1994, Division Two   Linton Brown
462.   v. Bournemouth, Home, 4-0,
        August 1989, Division Two   Andy Payton
463.   v. Southend United, Home, 4-0,
        March 2007, The Championship   Dean Windass
464.   v. Cambridge United, Away, 4-3,
        August 1993, Division Two   Dean Windass
465.   v. Chester City, Home, 3-0,
        September 1978, Division Three   Keith Edwards
466.   v. Darlington, Home, 3-2,
        August 1996, Division Three   Duane Darby
467.   v. Tranmere Rovers, Home, 6-1,
        December 2004, League One   Stuart Elliott
468.   v. Barnet, Home, 4-4,
        December 1993, Division Two   Dean Windass
469.   v. Bournemouth, Home, 4-0,
        January 1989, Division Two   Keith Edwards
470.   v. Birmingham City, Away, 4-2,
        April 1970, Division Two   Ken Houghton

KEITH EDWARDS

471.   1957
472.   Sheffield United
473.   Sheffield United (1975-78 and 1981-86)
474.   Carlisle United
475.   185 (2)
476.   86
477.   Stockport County
478.   Aberdeen
479.   Ian Porterfield
480.   Huddersfield Town

MATCH THE YEAR – 2

481.   Hull were champions of Division Three North   1933

482.	Hull won promotion to the Premier League	
	for the first time	2008
483.	John Kaye was appointed Hull City manager	1974
484.	George Maddison joined the Tigers from Spurs	1924
485.	Hull achieved their record win,	
	11-1 against Carlisle United	1939
486.	Craig Fagan joined Hull from Derby County,	
	his second spell at the club	2008
487.	Hull were champions of Division Three North	1949
488.	Hull made it to the FA Cup semi-finals	1930
489.	Brian Horton left as Hull manager	1988
490.	Bill Bradbury signed for the Tigers	
	from Birmingham City	1955

PHIL BROWN

491. *1959*
492. *Billy Ayre*
493. *652*
494. *Fullback*
495. *Bolton Wanderers*
496. *George Burley*
497. *Phil Parkinson*
498. *South Shields*
499. *Blackpool*
500. *The play-off final win over Bristol City at Wembley*

WINNING GOALS

501.	v. Plymouth Argyle, The Championship	
	February 2008, 1-0	Dean Windass
502.	v. Fulham, Home, Premier League,	
	August 2008, 2-1	Caleb Folan
503.	v. Darlington, Home, League Two,	
	August 1996, 3-2	Duane Darby
504.	v. Bristol City, Wembley, Play-off Final,	
	May 2008, 1-0	Dean Windass
505.	v. Crystal Palace, The Championship,	
	April 2008, 2-1	Ian Ashbee
506.	v. Wigan Athletic, Away, League Cup,	
	August 2007, 1-0	Stuart Elliott
507.	v. Crystal Palace, Home, League Cup,	
	September 1997, 2-1	Duane Darby

508.	v. Boston United, Away, League Two,	
	April 2003, 1-0	Stuart Elliott
509.	v. Scunthorpe United, Home, League Two,	
	April 2001, 2-1	Andy Holt
510.	v. Yeovil Town, Away, League Two,	
	May 2004, 2-1	Ian Ashbee

STUART PEARSON

511.	Hull
512.	Portsmouth
513.	Pancho
514.	Manchester United
515.	126 (3)
516.	Stockport County
517.	5
518.	West Ham United
519.	1982
520.	44

ANDY DAVIDSON

521.	1932
522.	Blackburn Rovers
523.	Right back
524.	Rangers
525.	520
526.	Division Three Championship in 1966
527.	Celtic
528.	18
529.	Jock
530.	3

POSITIONS IN THE LEAGUE – 3

531.	1967/1968	17th in Division Two
532.	1965/1966	1st in Division Three
533.	1963/1964	8th in Division Three
534.	1961/1962	10th in Division Three
535.	1959/1960	21st in Division Two
536.	1957/1958	5th in Division Three North
537.	1955/1956	22nd in Division Two

538.	1953/1954	15th in Division Two
539.	1951/1952	18th in Division Two
540.	1949/1950	7th in Division Two

GARRETH ROBERTS

541. **Hull**

542. **Bury**

543. **409 (5)**

544. **Defence, midfield and striker**

545. **Hull**

546. **47**

547. **KCFM**

548. **None, he only played for Hull City**

549. **478 (8)**

550. **1991**

2002/2003

551. **Stuart Elliott**

552. **£43.5 million**

553. **Jan Molby**

554. **Steve Melton**

555. **13th**

556. **Kidderminster Harriers**

557. **11**

558. **Hartlepool United**

559. **Justin Whittle**

560. **Carlisle United**

LEAGUE GOALSCORERS – 3

561.	Darren France	7
562.	Duane Darby	27
563.	Doug Clarke	79
564.	Neil Allison	3
565.	Russell Wainscoat	42
566.	Stuart Pearson	44
567.	Dale Roberts	6
568.	Ian McParland	7
569.	Viggo Jensen	51

570. Ray Daniel   3

LEAGUE ONE RUNNERS-UP – 2004/2005

571. Stuart Elliott
572. True
573. Craig Fagan
574. Luton Town
575. Tranmere Rovers
576. True
577. Kevin Ellison
578. True
579. Blackpool
580. 26

2001/2002

581. 11th
582. Gary Alexander
583. Lawrie Dudfield
584. 43
585. Cheltenham Town
586. Northwich Victoria
587. The League Cup
588. Huddersfield Town
589. Brighton & Hove Albion
590. Bristol Rovers

AGAINST WHICH TEAM?

591. Fulham
592. Stoke City
593. Bournemouth
594. Bournemouth
595. Northampton Town
596. Bury
597. Ipswich Town
598. Newport County
599. Southend United
600. Darlington

WHERE DID THEY GO? – 2

601.	John Bennion	Stockport County
602.	Kenny Gilbert	Ross County
603.	Les Metrie	Colchester United
604.	Alan Fettis	Macclesfield Town
605.	Dean Keates	Kidderminster
606.	Simon Dakin	Grantham Town
607.	Colin Alcide	York City
608.	Roy Carroll	Wigan Athletic
609.	Pat O'Connell	Manchester United
610.	David D'Auria	Chesterfield

DIVISION THREE RUNNERS-UP – 2003/2004

611. Doncaster Rovers
612. Torquay United and Huddersfield Town
613. Peter Taylor
614. Ben Burgess
615. 14
616. Damien Delaney
617. Darlington
618. Kidderminster Harriers
619. 25
620. Bristol Rovers

DIVISION THREE PROMOTION – 1984/1985

621. 3rd
622. False: they won one and lost two
623. Billy Whitehurst
624. Andy Flounders (14) and Stan McEwan (11)
625. Brian Horton
626. York City
627. Leyton Orient
628. Billy Whitehurst
629. Tony Norman
630. Billy Askew and Peter Skipper

1960s

631. Chris Chilton

632. **Cliff Britton**

633. **£200,000**

634. **Millwall**

635. **Top of the League**

636. **Chelsea**

637. **Ralph Gubbins**

638. **Northampton Town (23 September) and Crystal Palace (10 December)**

639. **Bolton Wanderers**

640. **Manchester City**

DIVISION FOUR RUNNERS-UP – 1982/1983

641. **Colin Appleton**

642. **Brian Marwood**

643. **Andy Flounders and Les Mutrie**

644. **Peter Skipper**

645. **York City**

646. **Stockport County**

647. **Andy Flounders**

648. **True: 3 wins and 2 draws**

649. **Tony Norman and John Davies**

650. **Wimbledon**

2000/2001

651. **6th**

652. **John Eyre**

653. **The bailiffs were called in and the Tigers were locked out of the ground**

654. **Leyton Orient**

655. **Mike Edwards**

656. **Exeter City**

657. **Macclesfield Town and York City**

658. **Andy Holt**

659. **Kidderminster Harriers**

660. **Darlington**

WHO AM I? - 2

661. **Geovanni Deiberson**

662. **Anthony Gardner**

663. **Bill McCracken**

664. **George Maddison**

665. **George Boateng**

666. **Ryan France**

667. **Ian Butcher**

668. **Chris Lee**

669. **Michael Turner**

670. **Eddie Gray**

HONOURS

671.	**Third Division Champions**	*1966*
672.	**Third Division North Champions**	*1949*
673.	**Fourth Division Runners-Up**	*1983*
674.	**League One Runners-Up**	*2005*
675.	**Third Division North Champions**	*1933*
676.	**Championship Play-Off Winners**	*2008*
677.	**Third Division Promotion**	*1985*
678.	**Won their first Premier League match**	*2008*
679.	**Third Division North Runners-Up**	*1959*
680.	**Division Three Runners-Up**	*2004*

BILLY ASKEW

681. **1959**

682. **6**

683. **Middlesbrough**

684. **19**

685. **1984/1985**

686. **Billy Whitehurst**

687. **247 (6)**

688. **Middlesbrough**

689. **False: Billy never scored an FA Cup goal**

690. **Newcastle United**

ANDY FLOUNDERS

691. **Hull**

692. **Hull City**

693. **3**

694. **126 (33)**

695. Brigg Town

696. Shrewsbury Town

697. 54

698. Scunthorpe United

699. 200

700. Northampton Town

POSITIONS THEY PLAYED

701.	Cliff Woodhead	Fullback
702.	Bill McNaughton	Centre forward
703.	Douglas Duncan	Outside left
704.	Ken Houghton	Midfield
705.	George Maddison	Goalkeeper
706.	Thomas Bleakley	Left half
707.	Cliff Hubbard	Forward
708.	John McQuillan	Left back
709.	Matt Bell	Fullback
710.	Martin Spendiff	Goalkeeper

LEAGUE APPEARANCES – 3

711.	Paul Hunter	37 (31)
712.	Steve Hoolickin	31
713.	Bobby McNeil	135 (3)
714.	Andy Mason	14 (12)
715.	Craig Lawford	45 (17)
716.	Tim Hotte	1 (4)
717.	Dennis Booth	121 (2)
718.	Dave King	65
719.	Duane Darby	79 (7)
720.	Stuart Young	11 (8)

RAICH CARTER

721. Sunderland

722. York City

723. Derby County

724. Football League Champions (1936) and FA Cup Winners (1937)

725. 30

726. 136

727.   57

728.   Leeds United

729.   The Raich Carter Sports Centre

730.   True

BOAZ MYHILL

731.   1982

732.   USA (Modesto, California)

733.   Aston Villa

734.   Macclesfield Town

735.   Peter Taylor

736.   Luxembourg

737.   Bradford City

738.   True

739.   51 (46 League and 5 Cup)

740.   Norwich City

WHERE DID THEY COME FROM? – 3

741.	Billy Askew	Gateshead
742.	Mark Greaves	Brigg Town
743.	Lee Warren	Rochdale
744.	Mike Quigley	Manchester City
745.	Billy Wilkinson	Stockton
746.	Craig Fagan	Derby County
747.	Malcolm Shotton	Barnsley
748.	George Boateng	Middlesbrough
749.	Mark Oxley	Rotherham
750.	Chris Galvin	Leeds United

BILLY BLY

751.   1920

752.   Rotherham United

753.   1961 (19 October)

754.   403

755.   Goalkeeper

756.   Division Three North Championship

757.   35

758.   Walker Celtic Amateurs

759.   True

760.   Weymouth

SQUAD NUMBERS - 2008/2009 - 2

761.	Richard Garcia	14
762.	Nick Barmby	8
763.	Boaz Myhill	1
764.	George Boateng	20
765.	Dean Marney	22
766.	Caleb Folan	18
767.	Tony Warner	26
768.	Ian Ashbee	4
769.	Michael Turner	6
770.	Bill Law	37

WHERE DID THEY GO? – 3

771.	Simon Trevitt	Guiseley
772.	Frank Bunn	Oldham Athletic
773.	Ken Knighton	Sheffield Wednesday
774.	Darryl Duffy	Swansea City
775.	Andy Duncan	Tottenham Hotspur
776.	Mike Hollifield	Tranmere Rovers
777.	Alan Fettis	Nottingham Forest
778.	Paul Anderson	Liverpool
779.	Leon Cort	Crystal Palace
780.	Jeff Wealands	Birmingham City

BIG WINS – 2

781.	v. Crewe Alexandra, Away, League Cup, August 2007	3-0
782.	v. Tranmere Rovers, Home, League, December 2004	6-1
783.	Northwich, Away, FA Cup, November 2001	5-2
784.	v. Southend United, Home, League, March 2007	4-0

785.	v. Swansea City, Home, League,	
	August 1997	7-4
786.	v. Whitby Town, Home, FA Cup,	
	November 1996	8-4
787.	v. Southampton, Home, League,	
	March 2008	5-0
788.	v. Darlington, Home, League,	
	August 2003	4-1
789.	v. Cheltenham Town, Home, League,	
	November 2001	5-1
790.	v. Crewe Alexandra, Home, League,	
	October 1994	7-1

CRAIG FAGAN

791.	Birmingham
792.	Derby County
793.	Birmingham City
794.	67 (13)
795.	15
796.	Jamaica
797.	Phil Brown
798.	£750,000
799.	Scunthorpe United
800.	Nick Barmby

NOTES

NOTES

NOTES

NOTES

NOTES

NOTES

NOTES

NOTES

www.apexpublishing.co.uk